30(

English Partsongs

Glees, rounds, catches, partsongs
1600-1900

selected and edited by
PAUL HILLIER

Faber Music
in association with
Faber & Faber

London & Boston

© 1983 by Faber Music Ltd
First published in 1983 by Faber Music Ltd
in association with Faber & Faber Ltd
3 Queen Square London WC1N 3AU
Reprinted in 1985
Music drawn by Michael Rowe
Printed in England by the Thetford Press
All rights reserved

Library of Congress Cataloging in Publication
Data.

Main entry under title:

300 years of English partsongs.

    For mixed voices unacc.
    1. Part-songs, English. 2. Glees, catches,
rounds, etc. 3. Choruses, Secular (Mixed voices),
Unaccompanied. 4. Vocal music – England. I.
Hillier, Paul. II. Title: Three hundred years of
English partsongs.
M1579.A14 1983   82-24182
ISBN 0-571-10045-7 (pbk.)

For Lena-Liis

Many of the items in this anthology have been recorded by
The Hilliard Ensemble under the editor's direction:
The Merry Companions, Saga 5477
The Romantic Englishman, Meridian E77002

Considerable ingenuity is sometimes required, especially in the earlier partsongs, to fit the words of the different verses to the music. There are often several equally satisfactory ways of doing this. The editor's own version may be discovered by reference to the small notes and broken slurs in the music. However it is not our intention to impose a particular version and choir directors should choose what they feel to be the most satisfactory solution in each case.

CONTENTS

INTRODUCTION

This anthology celebrates and explores the varieties of English partsong over a period of 300 years; a period when, after the death of Purcell, English music came increasingly to be regarded with scorn or indifference. The 'land without music' did not lack for performers or concerts or even composers, providing they were if possible from somewhere else. The truth seems to have been that English composers lacked the ability to conceive and sustain the sort of large forms that were the essence of the symphonic age. Although they may not have chosen to admit it, their greatest successes were scored when less was being attempted. A truer and more positive picture of English music is therefore drawn if we examine the smaller forms; church music would give us, in addition to the names represented here, that of Wesley. But as well as providing a source both of established favourites in the partsong repertoire and an introduction to some lesser known pieces (at least some of which might well become favourites), this collection represents a particular period of English music and, within that period, a particular tradition, varied but fundamentally continuous.

Most of the music included is essentially convivial in spirit and background – it was not always intended for concert performance, but like madrigals for the diversion of the singers themselves and their friends. Nevertheless the need to appeal to audiences has not been forgotten, and sufficient variety should be found to cater for many different occasions, both public and private. Similarly, while today mixed voices are the norm, much of this repertoire was conceived for male voices, especially the catches. Various suggestions are included to enable both mixed and male voice performance, and where any transposition or other alteration has been made, a full account is given.

The term 'partsong' is one of those that does duty for a variety of forms as well as being susceptible to particular definition. In the latter case it refers to the homophonic style in which the lower voices harmonise a melody carried in the top voice and movement is from chord to chord. In contrast to this is the polyphonic style, linear in conception, in which the voices are of more or less equal importance. But 'partsong' is also used to refer quite loosely to all vocal music in several parts, usually unaccompanied, and this usage is implied in the title of this collection partly for simplicity, and partly because there is a shared background and purpose (or lack of purpose) to all the music contained in it.

Even as the English madrigal was reaching its zenith in the mature works of Wilbye and Weelkes, a simpler style was beginning to assert itself, first apparent in the harmonised ayres and psalm settings of John Dowland. But the change was made most abruptly in the three publications of Thomas Ravenscroft in which a vein of popular balladry is tapped both with regard to the words and to the tunes which are harmonised with a naivety that is entirely sympathetic to the material. The collections are varied by the inclusion of rounds, even simpler in essence than the partsongs, of which 'Three Blind Mice' must be the most famous example, although a piece such as No. 5 indicates the type of invention with which Restoration composers were shortly to develop this miniature form into the catch.

Despite the commonplace origins of much of his material, Ravenscroft was nevertheless producing a cultivated product quite distinct from popular music-making. If his market was widening this was due in part to the diminishing costs of printing music and also to the growth of the middle classes who, with increasing leisure, acquired the musical literacy previously restricted to those with social eminence and more cash.

The 17th century catch is an extension of the traditional canonic principle encapsulated in rounds, the most significant development being that whereas a round tends to be a single melodic strand divided into short sections that fit together, in a catch each one of the sections is a complete melodic statement reaching a cadence before the next voice joins in. A further important characteristic is that the combination of these parts often produces an added meaning not otherwise apparent. In this way the voices seem to 'catch' at each other, a pun that was not lost on 17th century musicians and has been thought by some to explain the use of this term; however a likelier origin is the 14th century Italian caccia.

Collections of catches began to appear by the middle of the century; Hilton's 'Catch that catch can' in 1652; Playford's 'Musical Companion' in 1667 and 1673 followed by numerous later editions with added material. The musical dexterity and often brilliant word setting to be found in the catches, especially those of Purcell, have tended to take second place to the reputation gained by the words. Certainly this was an extrovert art and the following description of a tavern scene supports the popular image of singing catches and partsongs in a state of drunken abandon, an image which seems to accord well with the often bawdy character of the verse:

> Accordingly we stepped in, and in the kitchen found half a dozen of my friend's associates, in the height of their jollitry, as merry as so many Canterbridgians at Stirbridge Fair, or cobblers at a Crispin's Feast. After a friendly salutation, free from all foppish ceremonies, down we sat; and when a glass or two round had given fresh motion to our drowsy spirits, and abandoned all those careful thoughts which make man's life uneasy, wit begot wit and wine a thirsty appetite to each succeeding glass: then open were our hearts, and unconfined our fancies, my friend and I contributing our mites to add to the treasure of our felicity. Songs and catches crowned the night, and each man in his turn elevated his voice to fill our harmony with the more variety.[1]

It is indeed the legendary scurrilous nature of the words that during the 19th century restrained enthusiasm for the music, and which has caused much delight in this present and in some things more enlightened age. As an example of the Victorian attitude it is amusing to read the shocked tones of William Barrett (a devotee of the glee and more especially of Henry Bishop):

> Copies of these things which have survived the wreck of mighty time and the destroying hand of the conscientious are only to be found on the private shelves of the curious. The words in the majority of cases are either openly wanting in respectability, or else are capable of a meaning which would not give pleasure to a well-ordered mind, so that the works remain, an ever-shameful monument of the licentiousness of the age which gave them birth.[2]

We are fortunate that such attitudes no longer prevail, at least not so strongly; we can also admire the sheer skill and zest for life that made these 'things'. Such a consideration may also lead to the thought that catches and other social music of the period were appreciated for their musical and verbal wit and were very possibly sung accurately, in a state of relative sobriety – sometimes at least! It seems otherwise unlikely that Purcell, the most prolific of catch composers, would have expended his energy and wasted such good tunes on people too drunk to enjoy them.

The coffee-house, as well as the tavern, served as a popular setting for music-making, both vocal and instrumental, and all manner of business was transacted there, as Ned Ward again bears witness: 'Accordingly in we went, where a parcel of muddling muck-worms were as busy as so many rats in an old cheese-loft: some going, some coming, some scribbling, some talking, some drinking, some smoking, others jangling; and the whole like a Dutch Scoot or Boatswain's cabin.'[1] The renowned Samuel Pepys was especially fond of music and his diary records several occasions on which he joined in singing at a tavern, and he even comments on the absence of music at an important dinner at the Dolphin (27 October 1664).

During the 18th century catch composing continued though at a slower pace and mostly in imitation of the earlier style. One important exception to this, exemplified in the catches of Arne, lay in the development of the dramatic element in which, as in No. 15, two or three distinct characters are introduced with suitably amusing consequences.

But this was an age of clubs – the Noblemen and Gentlemen's Catch Club (still in existence) was founded in 1761 and two years later offered prizes for the best catch, canon and glee. This trend led to music as a more formal activity, less spontaneous in spirit, more artificial in expression. In particular it is the glee that now became an important musical form, and it remains a uniquely English creation. In its musical context the word 'glee' has nothing to do with being happy; it derives from the Anglo-Saxon 'gleo' meaning 'music', 'entertainment'. It may be defined as a vocal composition for three or more voices (usually one to a part, and unaccompanied), which is constructed in at least two sections often with different time signatures and contrasted in mood. The composers were often occupants of an organ loft or, like many of the singers, members of a cathedral choir; accordingly, glees were sung by male voices with some pretension to soloistic capacity and the top line was generally written for a male alto.

Samuel Webbe, of all the many composers who wrote glees, is most readily identifiable with the genre and has over two hundred glees to his credit. He was born in Minorca and later apprenticed to a London cabinet maker. Discovering his love of music almost by chance when repairing a harpsichord case (so the story goes), he abandoned his job to study music, supporting himself as a copyist. No. 19 offers a classic sampling of all that was admired in a glee – an irreproachably forthright text, a carefully controlled emotional declamation proceeding into a fugato section almost as if this were a miniature classical symphony; this then balanced by a peaceful and lyrical conclusion in the tonic major.

Unfortunately the musical substance of many glees fails to live up to the imposing seriousness of the composer's intention while others are instantly forgettable bucolic romps. This is a pity as there are exceptions and even if modern taste for the bulk of this repertoire is understandably cautious, it would be wrong and our own loss to overlook such a beautiful composition as No. 21 or such an entertaining piece as No. 24; indeed none of the glees included here is offered with apologies.

In John Stafford Smith we encounter a composer who was also a singer, being a chorister at the Chapel Royal and later a lay-clerk at Westminster Abbey; a scholar, who published in 1779 'A collection of English Songs, in score for 3 and 4 voices, composed about the year 1500. Taken from manuscripts of the same age' – primarily in fact the Fayrfax Manuscript; and an organist, becoming Master of the Children at the Chapel Royal in 1805. His glee, No. 22, opened each meeting of the Anacreontic Society which was founded in 1766 and met in the Crown & Anchor Tavern on the Strand 'for supper and the singing of catches, glees and songs'.

In a similar manner the Glee Club had begun to meet regularly by 1783, at first in members' houses, but then at the Newcastle Coffee House and later at the Crown & Anchor. For this society, Webbe's glee 'Glorious Apollo' served as general overture to the proceedings. Further societies such as the Madrigal Society, founded in 1741 by John Immyns, encouraged a revival of interest in English and Italian madrigals and also inspired the production of pieces in imitation, particularly by William Beale, Robert Pearsall and, later, John Stainer (another organist, composer and musicologist).

In time ladies were permitted to swell the ranks of these singing assemblies and the repertoire developed accordingly, further assisted by the now steady growth of choral societies throughout the land. By the 1850s there was even a professional group of vocalists – The Orpheus Vocal Union – available to perform Hatton's first collection of partsongs.

The Bristol Madrigal Society was founded in 1837 and one of its first members, singing tenor, was Robert Lucas Pearsall, whose own compositions became part of the society's repertoire. Pearsall was first and foremost a gentleman and conducted his various interests, which included archaeology and genealogy (of the aristocracy), as well as music, in the spirit of a liberal-minded but very thorough and conscientious amateur. In fact he took composition very seriously, especially after moving abroad for his health, and established something of a reputation in Germany. In 1842 he bought a castle – Schloss Wartensee – overlooking Lake Constance near the monastery of St Gall, where he lived for the rest of his life. He wrote orchestral and chamber music, but his partsongs remain his major achievement and belong in any self-respecting account of 19th century English music. Some were for double-choir ('Sir Patrick Spens' and 'Lay a Garland'), but most were for the now general four-part mixed chorus, that was well served by an expanding production of partsongs, harmonised ballads and imitation madrigals.

The later Victorians put more energy into larger forms, especially the oratorio and, in Sullivan's case, the stage. But in No. 30 Sullivan himself has composed a suitable elegy for the very essence of Victorian parlour music whose fragrant close harmonies seem to create with almost claustrophobic intensity the plush, interior atmosphere we associate with this age.

The more recent continuation of the partsong is beyond the scope of this volume, though it has certainly thrived. Passing through the hands of Elgar, Parry and Stanford it has assisted in what is cometimes known as the English renaissance. Delius, Vaughan Williams and later Britten have greatly expanded the harmonic idiom of the partsong and during the middle of the present century the growth of professional ensembles has further diversified the material that a group of mixed voices might expect to encounter. In turn it is hoped that the present collection will help add to this diversity by encouraging the awareness of a fascinating but relatively unknown area of English music.

PAUL HILLIER

[1] *The London Spy* by Edward Ward, London 1698.
[2] *English Glees and Partsongs – An enquiry into their historical development* by William A Barrett, London 1886.

1 By a bank as I lay

PARTSONG

THOMAS RAVENSCROFT

© 1983 by Faber Music Ltd

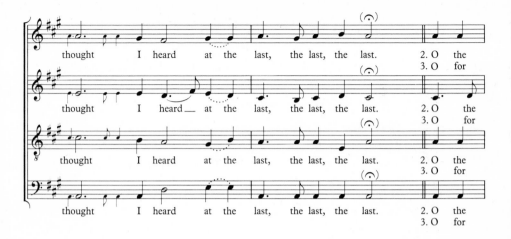

2   O the gentle nightingale (the nightingale),
    The lady and mistress of all musick,
    She sits down ever in the dale
    Singing with her notes smale,*
    Quavering them wonderful thick (full thick, full thick).

    *small

3   O for joy my spirits were quick (were quick, were quick),
    To hear the sweet bird how merrily she could sing,
    And said—good Lord defend
    England with thy most Holy hand,
    And save noble James our King (our King, our King).

2 There were three ravens

PARTSONG

THOMAS RAVENSCROFT

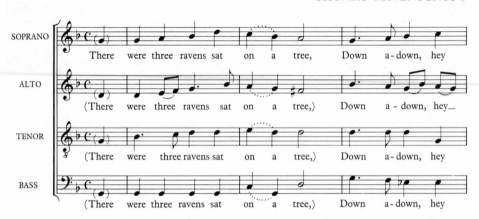

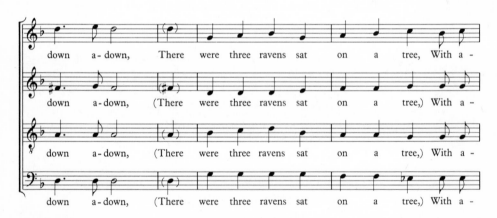

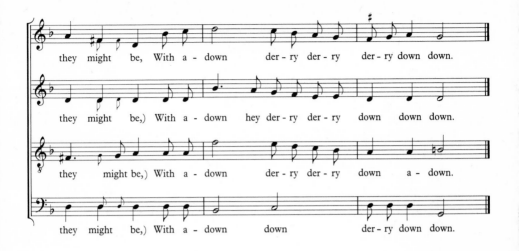

2 The one of them said to his mate,
   Down a-down (*etc.*),
   The one of them said to his mate,
   With a-down.
   The one of them said to his mate,
   Where shall we our breakfast take?
   With a-down (*etc.*).   *Remaining verses similarly.*

3 Down in yonder green field,
   There lies a knight slain under his shield.

4 His hounds they lie down at his feet,
   So well they can his master keep.

5 His hawks they fly so eagerly,
   There's no fowle dare come him nie.

6 Down there comes a fallow doe,
   As great with yong as she might goe.

7 She lift up his bloody hed,
   And kist his wounds that were so red.

8 She get him up upon her backe,
   And carried him to earthen lake.

9 She buried him before the prime,
   She was dead herself ere ev'nsong time.

10 God send every gentleman
   Such hawks, such hounds and such a leman.*

   *lover

3 We be three poor mariners

PARTSONG

THOMAS RAVENSCROFT

SOPRANO or ALTO

1. We be three poor ma - ri - ners, new - ly__ come from the

TENOR

1. We be three poor__ ma - ri - ners, new - ly come from__ the

BASS

1. We be three poor ma - ri - ners, new - ly come from the

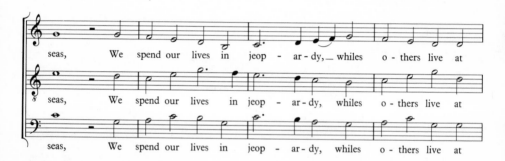

seas, We spend our lives in jeop - ar - dy,__ whiles o - thers live at

seas, We spend our lives in jeop - ar - dy, whiles o - thers live at

seas, We spend our lives in jeop - ar - dy, whiles o - thers live at

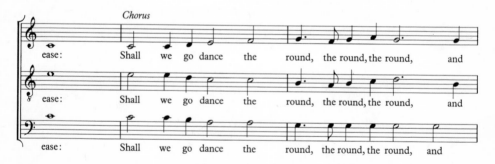

Chorus

ease: Shall we go dance the round, the round, the round, and

ease: Shall we go dance the round, the round, the round, and

ease: Shall we go dance the round, the round, the round, and

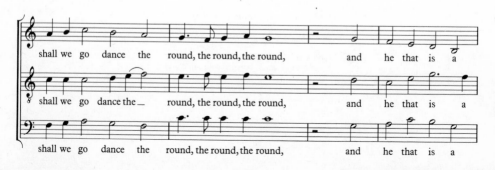

shall we go dance the round, the round, the round, and he that is a

shall we go dance the __ round, the round, the round, and he that is a

shall we go dance the round, the round, the round, and he that is a

bul - ly boy, come pledge me on the ground, the ground, the ground.

2   We care not for those martial men, that do our states
            disdain:
     But we care for those Marchant* men, which do our states
            maintain.
     Chorus

3   To them we dance this round, a round, to them we dance
            this round:
     And he that is a bully boy, come pledge me on the
            ground.
     Chorus

* Merchant

4 A Christmas Carroll

THOMAS RAVENSCROFT

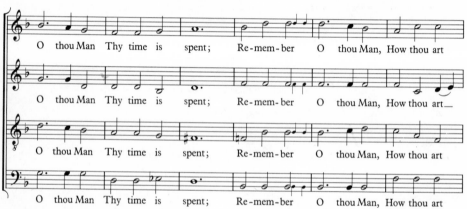

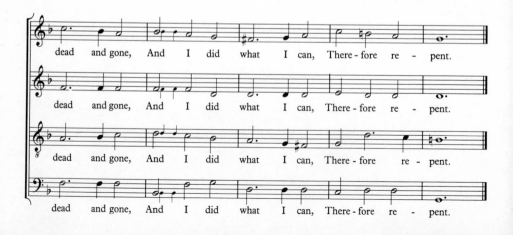

2 Remember Adam's fall
   O thou Man, O thou Man,
   Remember Adam's fall
   From heaven to hell;
   Remember Adam's fall
   How we were condemned all
   In hell perpetuall
   There for to dwell.

3 Remember God's goodnesse
   O thou Man, O thou Man,
   Remember God's goodnesse

   And his promise made;
   Remember God's goodnesse

   How he sent his sonne doubtlesse
   Our sinnes for to redresse,
   Be not afraid.

4 The angels all did sing
   O thou Man, O thou Man,

   The angels all did sing

   Upon the shepherd's hill;
   The angels all did sing

   Praises to our heav'nly King,
   And peace to man living
   With a good will.

5 The shepherds a-ma-zed was
   O thou Man, O thou Man,

   The shepherds a-ma-zed was

   To hear the angels sing;
   The shepherd a-ma-zed was
   How it should come to pass
   That Christ our Messias
   Should be our King.

6 To Bethlem they did go
   O thou Man, O thou Man,
   To Bethlem they did go
   The shepherds three;
   To Bethlem they did go
   To see where it were so
   Whether Christ were borne or no
   To set man free.

7 As th'angels before did say
   O thou Man, O thou Man,
   As th'angels before did say

   So it came to pass;
   As th'angels before did say

   They found a babe where it lay
   In a manger wrapt in hay,
   So poor he was.

8 In Bethlem he was born
   O thou Man, O thou Man,
   In Bethlem he was born
   For mankind sake;
   In Bethlem he was born
   For us that were forlorn
   And therefore took no scorn
   Our flesh to take.

9 Give thanks to God alway
   O thou Man, O thou Man,
   Give thanks to God alway

   With heart most joyfully;
   Give thanks to God alway
   For this our happy day,
   Let all men sing and say
   Holy, holy.

5 A Round of three Country dances in one

THOMAS RAVENSCROFT

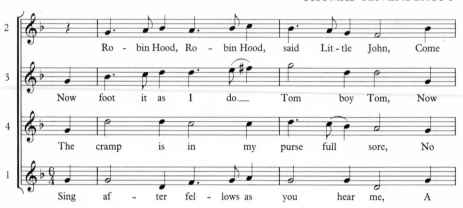

Ro - bin Hood, Ro - bin Hood, said Lit - tle John, Come

Now foot it as I do— Tom boy Tom, Now

The cramp is in my purse full sore, No

Sing af - ter fel - lows as you hear me, A

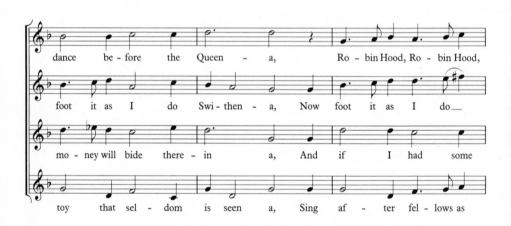

dance be - fore the Queen - a, Ro - bin Hood, Ro - bin Hood,

foot it as I do Swi - then - a, Now foot it as I do—

mo - ney will bide there - in a, And if I had some

toy that sel - dom is seen a, Sing af - ter fel - lows as

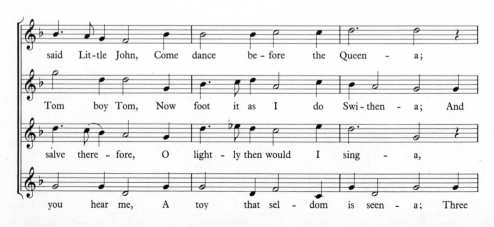

said Lit - tle John, Come dance be - fore the Queen - a;

Tom boy Tom, Now foot it as I do Swi - then - a; And

salve there - fore, O light - ly then would I sing - a,

you hear me, A toy that sel - dom is seen - a; Three

6 Gather your rosebuds while you may

AYRE

ROBERT HERRICK   WILLIAM LAWES

2   The glorious lamp of heaven, the sun, The higher he's a-getting
    The sooner will his race be run, And nearer he's to setting.

3   That age is best that is the first, While youth and blood are warmer,
    Expect not the last and worst, Time still succeeds the former.

4   Then be not coy, but use your time, And while you may go marry,
    For having once but lost your prime, You may for ever tarry.

*See notes on page 86

7 Tho' I am young

AYRE

NICHOLAS LANIER

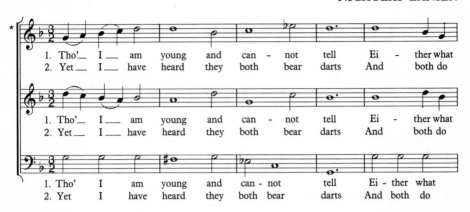

1. Tho'— I — am young and can - not tell Ei - ther what
2. Yet— I — have heard they both bear darts And both do

love or death is well, And then a - gain I have been told
aim at hu - man hearts, So that I fear they do but bring

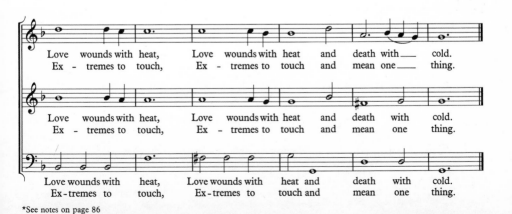

Love wounds with heat, Love wounds with heat and death with___ cold.
Ex - tremes to touch, Ex - tremes to touch and mean one___ thing.

*See notes on page 86

8 When the cock begins to crow

TRIO

HENRY PURCELL

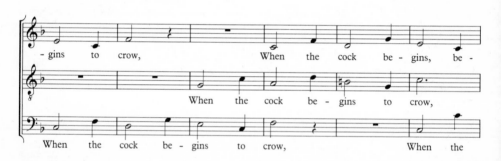

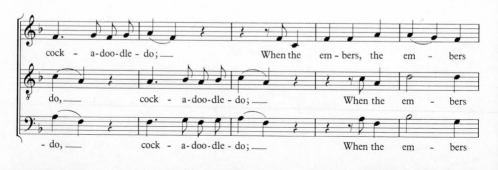

leave ___ to ___ glow, And the owl cries, ___

leave to glow, And the owl cries, to whit to who, to

leave to glow, And the owl cries, to whit to who, to

to whit to who, to whit to who, to whit to who. ___ When

whit to who, to who, to whit to who, to whit to who. ___ When

whit to who, to who, to whit to who, to whit to who. ___ When

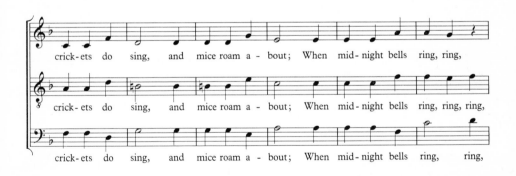

crick-ets do sing, and mice roam a-bout; When mid-night bells ring, ring,

crick-ets do sing, and mice roam a-bout; When mid-night bells ring, ring, ring,

crick-ets do sing, and mice roam a-bout; When mid-night bells ring, ring,

ring, ring, ring, ring, ring, ring, ring, ring To call the de -

ring, ring, ring, ring, ring, ring, ring To call the de -

ring, ring, ring, ring, ring, ring, ring To call the de -

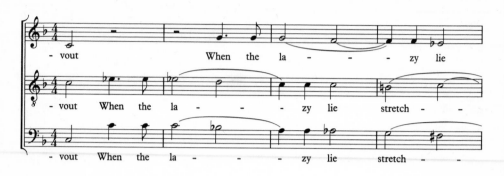

- vout When the la - - zy lie
- vout When the la - - zy lie stretch - -
- vout When the la - - zy lie stretch - -

stretch - ing, and think it no harm; their zeal is so cold and their
- ing, and think it no harm; their zeal is so cold and their
- ing, and think it no harm; their zeal is so cold and their

beds are so warm; When the long la - zy slut Has not made the par - lour
beds are so warm; When the long la - zy slut Has not made the par - lour
beds are so warm; When the long la - zy slut Has not made the par - lour

clean; No wa - ter on the hearth is put, But all, all, all,
clean; No wa - ter on the hearth is put, But all,
clean; No wa - ter on the hearth is put, But all,

all — things in dis-or-der seen, all things in dis-or-der seen, all things

all things in dis-or-der seen, all things in dis-or-der seen, all things in— dis -

all, all things in dis-or-der seen, all things in dis-or-der seen,

all things in— dis - or - der seen. Then we trip it, trip it, trip it,

- or - - - der— seen. Then we trip it, trip it, trip it,

all things in dis - or - der seen. Then we trip it, trip it, trip it,

trip it, trip it, trip it, trip it, trip it, trip it, trip it, trip it, trip it, trip it, trip it round the

trip it, trip it, trip it, trip it, trip it, trip it, trip it, trip it, trip it, trip it, trip it round the

trip it, trip it, trip it, trip it, trip it, trip it, trip it, trip it, trip it, trip it, trip it round the

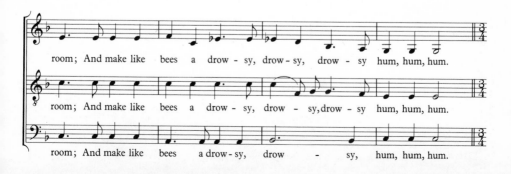

room; And make like bees a drow - sy, drow-sy, drow - sy hum, hum, hum.

room; And make like bees a drow - sy, drow - sy, drow - sy hum, hum, hum.

room; And make like bees a drow-sy, drow - sy, hum, hum, hum.

Be she Bet - ty, Nan, or Sue, We make her, make her

Be she Bet - ty, Nan,— or Sue, We make her, make her

Be she Bet - ty, Nan, or Sue, We make her, make her

of an - o - ther hue, And pinch her, pinch her, pinch her

of an - o - ther hue, And pinch her, pinch her, pinch her

of an - o - ther hue, And pinch her, pinch her, pinch her

black and blue, and pinch her, pinch her, pinch her black and

black and blue, and pinch her, pinch her, pinch her black and

black and blue, and pinch her, pinch her, pinch her black and

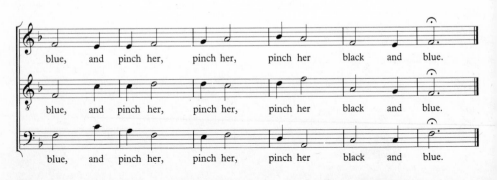

blue, and pinch her, pinch her, pinch her black and blue.

blue, and pinch her, pinch her, pinch her black and blue.

blue, and pinch her, pinch her, pinch her black and blue.

9 I gave her cakes and I gave her ale

CATCH

HENRY PURCELL

1. I gave her cakes and I gave her ale and I

2. gave her beads and brace-lets fine, And I

3. Mer-ry my hearts, mer-ry my cocks, mer-ry my sprights, mer-ry mer-ry, mer-ry,

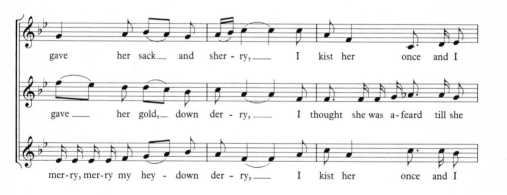

gave her sack and sher-ry, I kist her once and I

gave her gold, down der-ry, I thought she was a-feard till she

mer-ry, mer-ry my hey-down der-ry, I kist her once and I

kist her twice And we were won - drous mer-ry. I

strok'd my beard, And we were won - drous mer-ry.

kist her twice And we were won - drous mer-ry. I

10 Since time so kind to us does prove

CATCH

HENRY PURCELL

1. 'Since Time so kind to us does prove, so kind to us does prove, do not, my dear, re-fuse my love.'

2. 'What do you mean? Oh, fye! Nay, what do you do? You're the stran - gest man that e'er I knew!'

3. 'I must, I must, I can't for - bear, I can't, I can't for - bear! Lye still, lye still, my dear.'

11 Here lies a woman

CATCH

JOHN HILTON

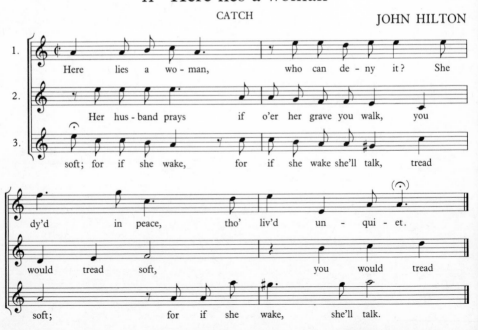

1. Here lies a wo - man, who can de - ny it? She dy'd in peace, tho' liv'd un - qui - et.

2. Her hus - band prays if o'er her grave you walk, you would tread soft, you would tread

3. soft; for if she wake, for if she wake she'll talk, tread soft; for if she wake, she'll talk.

12 Here's that will challenge all the fair

CATCH

HENRY PURCELL

1. Here's that will chal - lenge all the fair, come

2. Here's Di - ves and La - za - rus, and the world's cre - a - tion,

3. To - ta, to - ta, tot, goes the lit - tle pen - ny trum - pet,

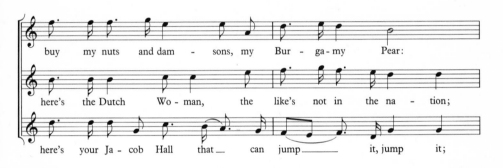

buy my nuts and dam - sons, my Bur - ga - my Pear:

here's the Dutch Wo - man, the like's not in the na - tion;

here's your Ja - cob Hall that can jump it, jump it;

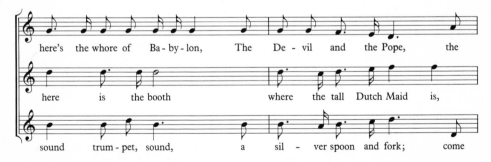

here's the whore of Ba - by - lon, The De - vil and the Pope, the

here is the booth where the tall Dutch Maid is,

sound trum - pet, sound, a sil - ver spoon and fork; come

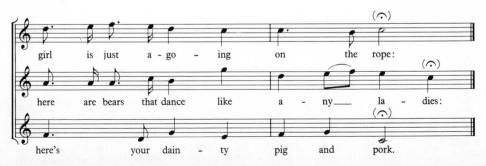

girl is just a - go - ing on the rope:

here are bears that dance like a - ny la - dies:

here's your dain - ty pig and pork.

13 My man John

CATCH

The Riddle explain'd:
Maid Mary having broke the handle of her hair broom, and hearing that
man John had a long stick that would fitt it, desir'd him to put it in for her.

JOHN ECCLES

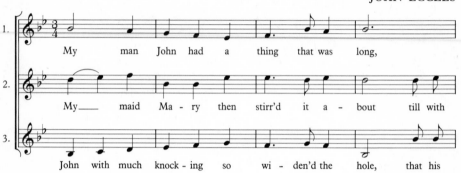

1. My man John had a thing that was long,

2. My____ maid Ma - ry then stirr'd it a - bout till with

3. John with much knock - ing so wi - den'd the hole, that his

My maid Ma - ry had a thing that was hai - ry,

stir - ring and stir - ring at length it came out, but

long thing slip'd out still in spight of his soul, 'till

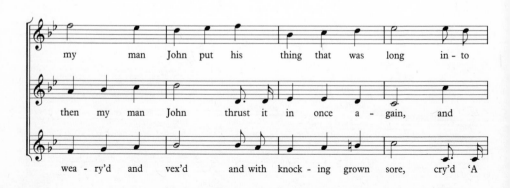

my man John put his thing that was long in - to

then my man John thrust it in once a - gain, and

wea - ry'd and vex'd and with knock - ing grown sore, cry'd 'A

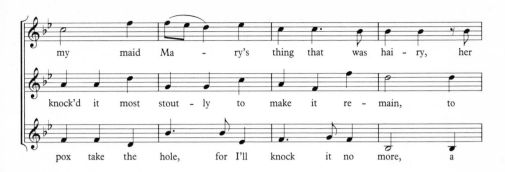

my maid Ma - ry's thing that was hai - ry, her

knock'd it most stout - ly to make it re - main, to

pox take the hole, for I'll knock it no more, a

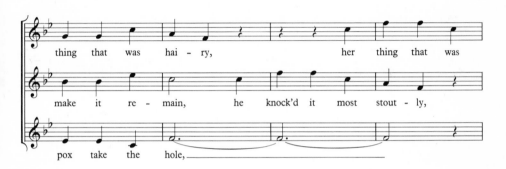

thing that was hai - ry, her thing that was

make it re - main, he knock'd it most stout - ly,

pox take the hole,

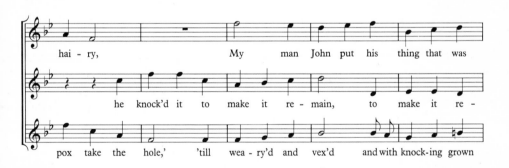

hai - ry, My man John put his thing that was

he knock'd it to make it re - main, to make it re -

pox take the hole,' 'till wea - ry'd and vex'd and with knock-ing grown

long in - to my maid Ma - ry's thing that was hai - ry.

- main, he knock'd it most stout - ly to make it re - main. But

sore, cry'd 'A pox take the hole, for I'll knock it no more.'

14 Which is the properest day to drink

GLEE

THOMAS ARNE

15 The Street Intrigue

CATCH

THOMAS ARNE

1. Hark you, my Dear, come hi - ther
2. O fie, Sir, I
3. So Mis - tress Minx, have I caught you, have I

my dear, come hi - ther, af - ford me a mo - ment's de -
can't Sir, I can't Sir, Lord what will the neigh - bours
caught you? Hey day! what do - ings, what do - ings are

- lay. Where would you run, say whi - ther, shall
say? They'd all tell my Mo - ther I
here? Come home you slut, come home, 'od rot it, come home and

28

16 Elegy on the death of Mr. Shenstone

GLEE

THOMAS ARNE

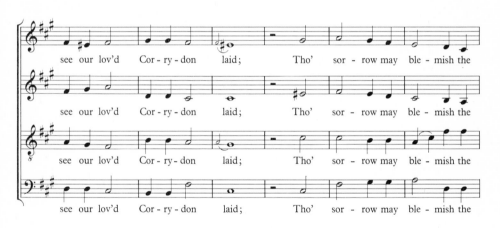

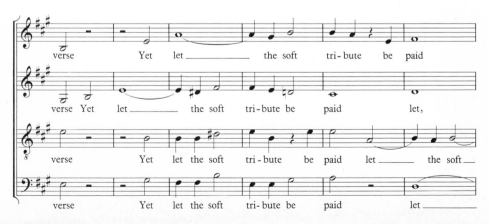

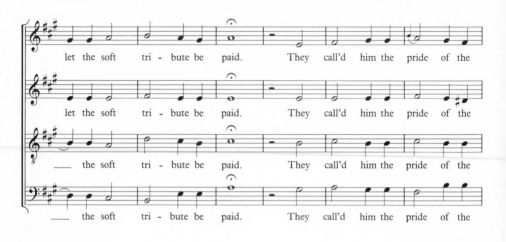

let the soft tri - bute be paid. They call'd him the pride of the

let the soft tri - bute be paid. They call'd him the pride of the

___ the soft tri - bute be paid. They call'd him the pride of the

___ the soft tri - bute be paid. They call'd him the pride of the

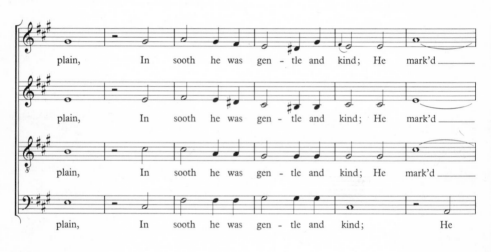

plain, In sooth he was gen - tle and kind; He mark'd _____

plain, In sooth he was gen - tle and kind; He mark'd _____

plain, In sooth he was gen - tle and kind; He mark'd _____

plain, In sooth he was gen - tle and kind; He

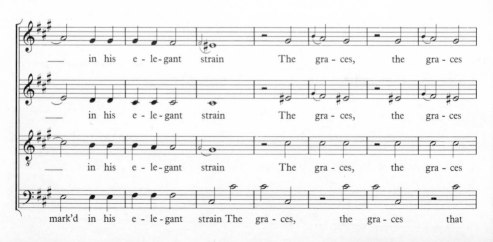

___ in his e - le - gant strain The gra - ces, the gra - ces

___ in his e - le - gant strain The gra - ces, the gra - ces

___ in his e - le - gant strain The gra - ces, the gra - ces

mark'd in his e - le - gant strain The gra - ces, the gra - ces that

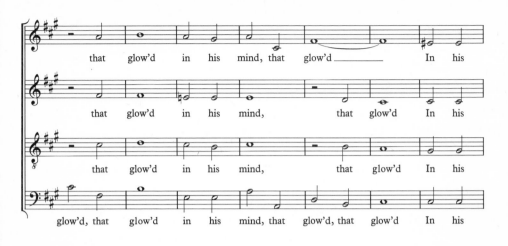

that glow'd in his mind, that glow'd _____ In his

that glow'd in his mind, that glow'd In his

that glow'd in his mind, that glow'd In his

glow'd, that glow'd in his mind, that glow'd, that glow'd In his

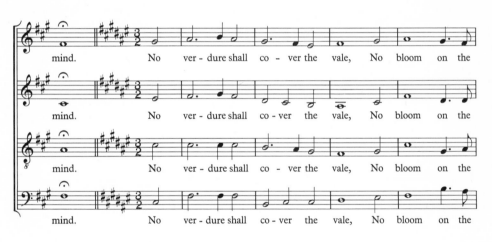

mind. No ver - dure shall co - ver the vale, No bloom on the

mind. No ver - dure shall co - ver the vale, No bloom on the

mind. No ver - dure shall co - ver the vale, No bloom on the

mind. No ver - dure shall co - ver the vale, No bloom on the

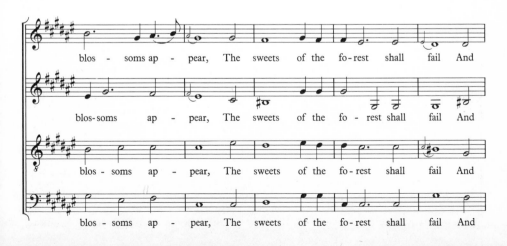

blos - soms ap - pear, The sweets of the fo - rest shall fail And

blos-soms ap - pear, The sweets of the fo - rest shall fail And

blos - soms ap - pear, The sweets of the fo - rest shall fail And

blos - soms ap - pear, The sweets of the fo - rest shall fail And

win - ter dis - co - lour the year. No birds in our hedg - es shall___

win - ter dis - co - lour the___ year. No birds in our hedg - es shall

win - ter dis - co - lour the year. No birds in our hedg - es shall

win - ter dis - co - lour the year. No birds in our hedg - es shall

sing Our hedg - es so vo - cal be - fore, Since he that should

sing Our hedg - es so vo - cal be - fore, Since he that should

sing Our hedg - es so vo - cal be - fore, Since he that should

sing Our hedg - es so vo - cal be - fore, Since he that should

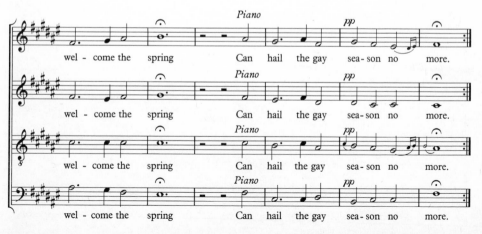

wel - come the spring Can hail the gay sea - son no more.

wel - come the spring Can hail the gay sea - son no more.

wel - come the spring Can hail the gay sea - son no more.

wel - come the spring Can hail the gay sea - son no more.

17 Epitaph

CATCH

JONATHAN BATTISHILL

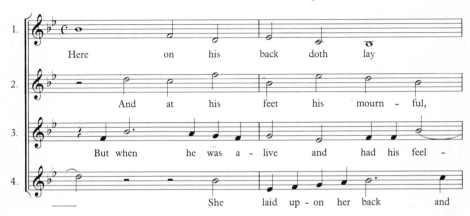

1. Here on his back doth lay

2. And at his feet his mourn - ful,

3. But when he was a - live and had his feel -

4. _____ She laid up - on her back and

Sir An - drew Keel - ing, doth lay,

mourn - ful la - dy kneel - ing, his la - dy,

- - ing, and had his feel - ing, When _____ he was a - live and had _____

he _____ was kneel - ing, and he was kneel - ing, up -

doth lay, Sir An - drew Keel - ing;

his la - dy, _____ his mourn - ful la - dy kneel - ing.

_____ his feel - ing, and had his feel - - ing, _____

on her _____ back, up - on her back and he was kneel - ing.

18 Sylvia blushes when I woo her

GLEE

PRIOR

JONATHAN BATTISHILL

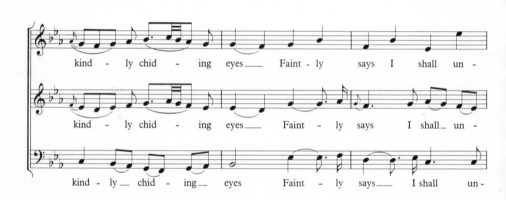

*See notes on page 86

19 Discord! Dire sister

GLEE

SAMUEL WEBBE

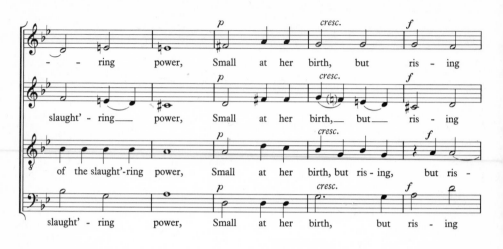

ring power, Small at her birth, but ris - ing
slaught' - ring___ power, Small at her birth,__ but__ ris - ing
of the slaught'-ring power, Small at her birth, but ris - ing, but ris -
slaught' - ring power, Small at her birth, but ris - ing

ev' - ry hour. While scarce the skies her hor-rid head can bound, She
ev' - ry hour. While scarce the skies her hor-rid head can bound, She
- ing ev'- ry hour.___ her hor-rid head can bound, She
ev' - ry hour. While scarce the skies her hor-rid head can bound, She

stalks on Earth and shakes the world a - round. But love - ly
stalks on Earth and shakes the world a - round. But love - ly
stalks, she stalks on Earth and shakes the world a - round. But love - ly
stalks on Earth and shakes the world a - round. But love - ly

20 Breathe soft ye winds

GLEE

Words from The Spectator

STEPHEN PAXTON

Andante affettuoso

*See notes on page 86

21 Come, gentle zephyr

GLEE

RAUNIE

WILLIAM HORSLEY

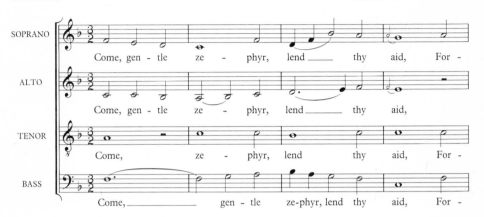

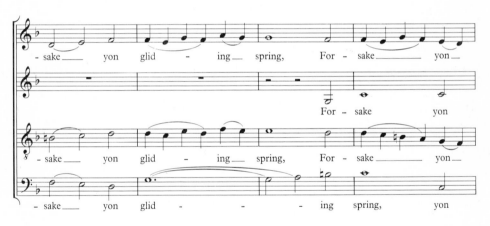

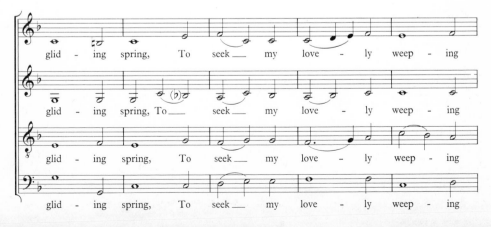

maid, Oh! Wave thy swift-est wing,
maid, Oh! Wave thy swift-est wing, Oh! Wave thy swift-est
maid, Oh! Wave thy swift-est wing,
maid, Oh! Wave thy swift-est wing, Oh! Wave thy swift-est, swift-est

Oh! Wave thy swift-est wing, Oh! Wave thy swift-est
wing, Oh! Wave thy swift-est wing, Wave, Oh! Wave thy swift-est
thy swift-est wing, Oh! Wave thy swift-est wing, thy swift-est
wing, Oh! Wave thy swift-est, swift - est

wing. wing. And when you find the
wing. wing. And when you find the
wing. wing. And when you find the
wing. wing. And when you find the

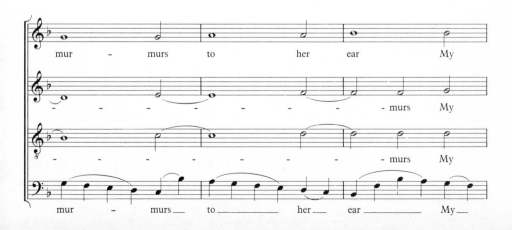

sighs, my vows re - veal, In plain - tive
sighs, my vows re - veal, In mur -
sighs, my vows re - veal, In mur -
sighs, my vows re - veal, In plain - tive

mur - murs to her ear. My sighs, my
- - - - - murs, My sighs, my
- - - - - murs, My sighs, my
mur - murs to her ear, My sighs, my

vows re - veal, My sighs, my vows re - veal.
vows re - veal, My sighs, my vows re - veal.
vows re - veal, My sighs, my vows re - veal.
vows re - veal, My sighs, my vows re - veal.

22 The Anacreontick Song

GLEE

RALPH TOMLINSON

JOHN STAFFORD SMITH

48

Ve - nus, the Myr - tle of __ Ve - nus __ with __ Bac - chus' s __ Vine.

The Myr - tle of __ Ve - nus with Bac - chus' s __ Vine.

with Bac - chus' s Vine.

2 The news through Olympus immediately flew,
When Old Thunder pretended to give himself airs—
If these mortals are suffered their scheme to pursue,
The Devil a Goddess will stay above stairs.
        'Hark!' already they cry,
        'In transports of joy,
Away to the sons of Anacreon we'll fly.
And there, with good fellows, we'll learn to entwine
The myrtle of Venus with Bacchus's vine.

3 'The yellow hair'd God and nine fusty maids
From Helicon's banks will incontinent flee,
Idalia will boast of tenantless Shades,
And the bi-forked hill a mere desert will be,
        My thunder no fear on't
        Shall soon do its errand,
And soundly I'll swinge the ringleaders I warrant,
I'll trim the young dogs, for thus daring to twine
The myrtle of Venus with Bacchus's vine.'

4 Apollo rose up and said 'Prythee ne'er quarrel,
Good king of the gods with my vot'ries below:
Your thunder is useless'—then shewing his laurel
Cried 'Sic evitabile fulmen, you know!
        Then over each head
        My laurels I'll spread,
So my sons from your crackers no mischief shall dread,
While snug in their club-room they jovially twine
The myrtle of Venus with Bacchus's vine.'

5 Next Momus got up with his risible Phiz,
And swore with Apollo he'd cheerfully join,
'The full tide of harmony still shall be his,
But the song and the catch and the laugh shall be mine;
        Then Jove be not jealous
        Of these honest fellows'.
Cried Jove 'We relent since the truth you now tell us,
And swear by old Styx that they long shall entwine
The myrtle of Venus with Bacchus's vine.

6 Ye sons of Anacreon then join hand in hand;
Preserve Unanimity, Friendship and Love!
Tis yours to support what's so happily plann'd,
You've the sanction of Gods and the fiat of Jove.
        While thus we agree,
        Our toast let it be,
May our club flourish happy, united and free!
And long may the sons of Anacreon entwine
The myrtle of Venus with Bachus's vine.

23 Foresters, sound the cheerful horn

GLEE

JOHN PETRE

HENRY ROWLEY BISHOP

SOPRANO

Fo-res-ters sound the cheer-ful horn Hark to the woods a - way!___ DI-

ALTO

Fo-res-ters sound the cheer - ful horn Hark to the woods a - way!___ DI-

TENOR

Fo-res-ters sound the cheer-ful horn Hark to the woods a - way!___

BASS

Fo-res-ters sound the cheer-ful horn Hark to the woods a - way!___ DI-

- A - NA with___ her nymphs this morn Will hunt the stag___ to bay.___

- A - NA with___ her nymphs this morn Will hunt the stag to bay.___

Will hunt the stag to bay.___

- A - NA with her nymphs this morn Will hunt the stag to bay.___

bay.___ While

bay.___ While

bay.___ At length re-turn'd from health-ful chase Let BAC-CHUS crown the day,___ While

bay.___ At length re-turn'd from health-ful chase Let BAC-CHUS crown the day,___

24 Crows in the cornfield

GLEE

THOMAS PHILLIPS

*See notes on page 86

Andante più parlante

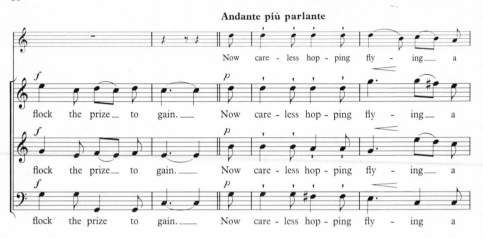

Now care - less hop - ping fly - ing — a
flock the prize — to gain. — Now care - less hop - ping fly - ing — a
flock the prize — to gain. — Now care - less hop - ping fly - ing — a
flock the prize to gain. — Now care - less hop - ping fly - ing a

young Crow light and gay, — So care - less light — and gay he hops!
young Crow light and gay, — So care - less light and gay he hops!
young Crow light and gay, — So care - less light and gay he hops! So care - less light — and
young Crow light and gay, — So care - less light — and gay he hops! So care - less light — and

he hops! So care - less light — and gay he hops! So care - less light and gay, — So
he hops! So care - less light — and gay he hops! So care - less light and gay, — So
gay he hops! So care - less light — and gay he hops! So care - less light and gay, — So
gay he hops! So care - less light and gay he hops! So care - less light and gay, — So

60

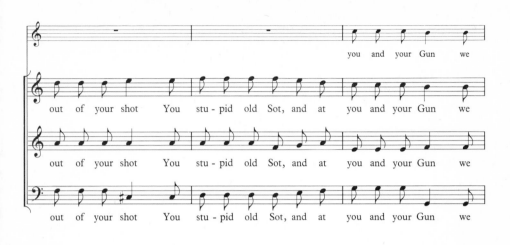

25 Purple glow the forest mountains

PARTSONG

from the German
of Mathison

ROBERT LUCAS PEARSALL

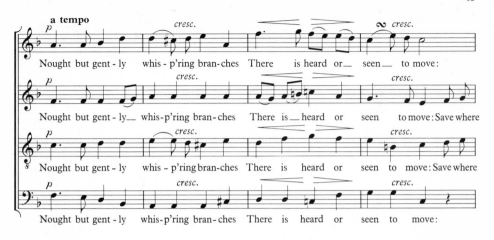

64

Minore

On such an eve - ning

I ____ shall hear thy

Soon, per - haps, on such__ an__ eve - ning__ I shall hear__ thy

Soon, per - haps, on such__ an__ eve - ning I shall hear thy__

Sad - ly sing - ing to the ro - ses__

voice__ re - sound,__ Sad - ly sing - ing____ to the ro - ses

voice__ re - sound,__ Sad - ly sing - ing to the

voice__ re - sound,__ Sad - ly sing - ing

Majore

Which ____ my__ ear - ly grave surround. Then my soul shall lis - ten to ____

Which ____ my ear - ly grave surround. Then my soul shall lis - ten to ____ thy

ro - ses my ear - ly grave surround. Then my soul shall lis - ten to thy

Which ____ my ear - ly grave surround. Then my soul ____ shall

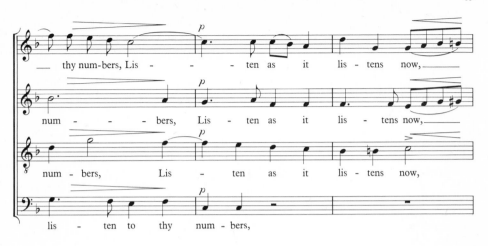

26 O who will o'er the downs so free

PARTSONG

ROBERT LUCAS PEARSALL

nei - ther door nor bolt Shall part my own true love from me. I saw her bow'r at

nei - ther door nor bolt Shall part my own true love from me. I saw her bow'r at

nei - ther door nor bolt Shall part my own true love from me. I saw her bow'r at

nei - ther door nor bolt Shall part my own true love from me. I saw her bow'r at

twi - light grey, 'Twas guard - ed safe and sure, I saw her bow'r at

twi - light grey, 'Twas guard - ed safe and sure, I saw her bow'r at

twi - light grey, 'Twas guard - ed safe and sure, I saw her bow'r at

twi - light grey, 'Twas guard - ed safe and sure, I saw her bow'r at

break of day, 'Twas guard - ed then no more! The var - lets they were

break of day, 'Twas guard - ed then no more! The var - lets they were

break of day, 'Twas guard - ed then no more! The var - lets they were

break of day, 'Twas guard - ed then no more! The var - lets they were

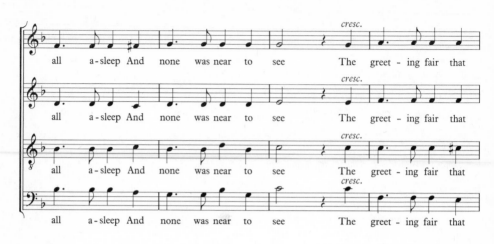

all a-sleep And none was near to see The greet-ing fair that

pass-ed there Be-tween my love and me. I pro-mis'd her to come at night With

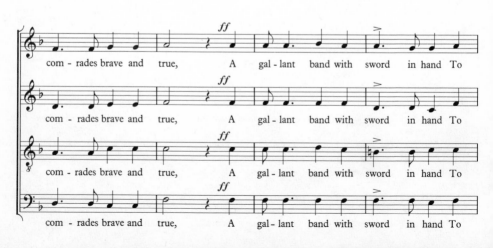

com-rades brave and true, A gal-lant band with sword in hand To

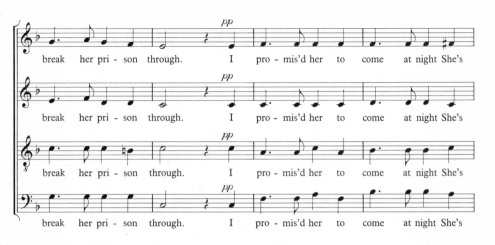

break her pri - son through. I pro - mis'd her to come at night She's

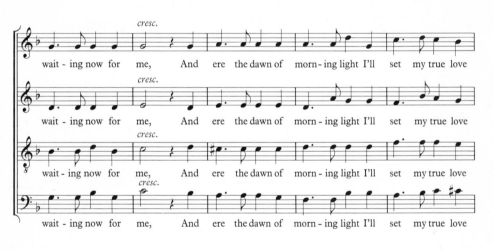

wait - ing now for me, And ere the dawn of morn - ing light I'll set my true love

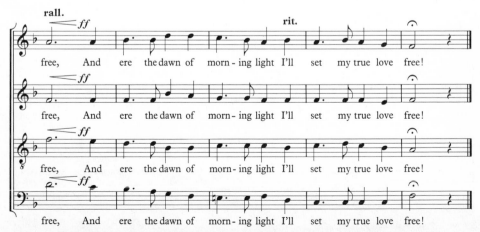

free, And ere the dawn of morn - ing light I'll set my true love free!

27 When evening's twilight

PARTSONG

JOHN LIPTROT HATTON

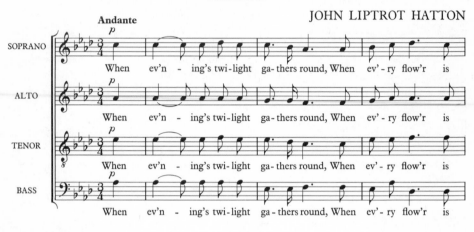

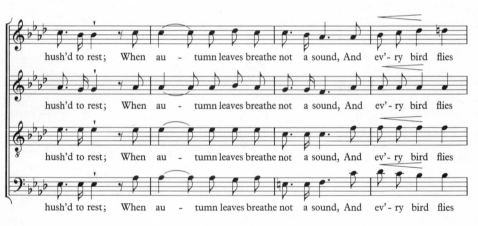

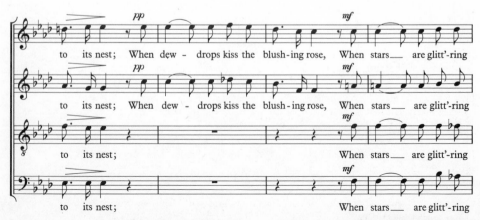

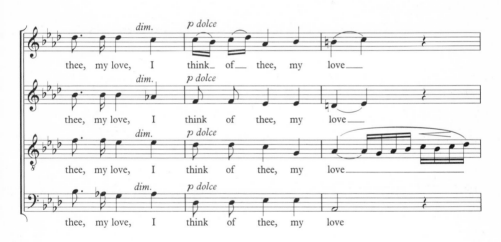

* May be sung by tenor and bass

28 Sweet and low

LULLABY

ALFRED LORD TENNYSON

JOSEPH BARNBY

2 Sleep and rest, sleep and rest,
    Father will come to thee soon;
    Rest, rest, on mother's breast,
    Father will come to thee soon;
    Father will come to his babe in the nest,
    Silver sails all out of the west
    Under the silver moon!
    Sleep, my little one, sleep my pretty one, sleep.

29 Cupid, look about thee

A FA-LA

Words from Robinson's
'New Citheon Lessons'

JOHN STAINER

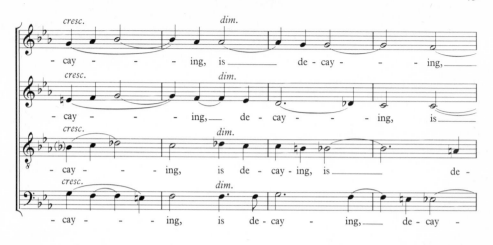

Tempo I

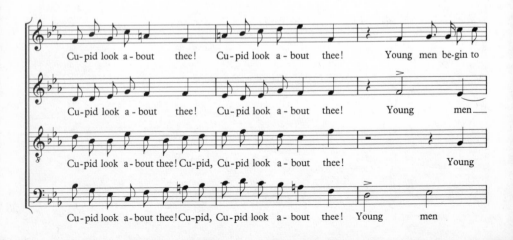

fa la la la, fa la la la, fa la la, fa la la la la,

la la la la, fa la la la, fa la la, fa la la

la la la la, fa la la la la, fa la la, fa la la la,

la, fa la, fa la la, fa la la la,

fa la la la la, fa la la la la, fa la la la la la la, fa la la la,

la, fa la la la, fa la la la la la la la la, fa la la la la,

fa la la la, fa la la la, fa la la la la la, fa la la la la,

fa la la la, fa la la la, fa la la la la la, fa la la,

Rather slow   **rall.**

fa la la la. Fa la la la la la la la.

fa la la la. Fa la la la la la la la la la.

fa la la. Fa la la la la la la

fa la la. Fa la la la la la la la.

30 The long day closes

PARTSONG

HENRY F. CHORLEY

ARTHUR SULLIVAN

*The small notes in the Bass part are intended for use as *additional* notes, when the Part-Song is performed by a Chorus.

NOTES

1 From *Freeman's Songs of Four Voices, Deuteromelia* (1609).
2 From *Country Pastimes, Melismata* (1611) – the words in parenthesis are omitted in the original, suggesting that the lower voices might hum (repeated notes being held through) and join in the choruses 'down-a-down'. An ancient ballad of Celtic origin – see also 'The twa corbies' and 'Corpus Christi' in The Faber Book of Ballads, ed. Matthew Hodgart.
3 From *Freeman's Songs of Three Voices, Deuteromelia* (1609).
4 From *Country Pastimes, Melismata* (1611).
5 From *Pammelia* (1609) – can be performed by mixed voices, though the 'ground' should be in the bass and starts alone, the other voices entering as numbered. A suggested disposition is 1 (ground) bass, 2 alto, 3 soprano, 4 tenor.
6, 7 From *Short Ayres or Songs for Three Voyces, Playford's 2nd Book of Ayres* (1652) – can be sung ssb, stb or ttb, with continuo or unaccompanied.
8 From an C18th MS score – the ascription to Henry Purcell is doubtful; the editor of the Purcell Society Edition, vol. XXII suggests it was intended as an insert for The Fairy Queen.
9 From *The Catch Club or Merry Companions* (1733) – originally in C major.
10 From *The Catch Club or Merry Companions* (1733) – originally in A minor.
11 From *Catch that Catch Can* (1633).
12 From *The 2nd Book of the Catch Club or Merry Companions* (1740).
13 From *The Catch Club or Merry Companions* (1733) – if the words are likely to give offence it might be advisable to read the 'explanation' first, or choose another piece.
14 From *A 2nd Collection of Catches* (1766) – this piece, entitled a glee, although it has many characteristics of a catch, gained a prize medal in 1765. Originally in G major. Best sung by four equal voices.
15 From *A Collection of Catches* (1764) – best portrayed by three distinct characters (the middle line by a woman), the top line being sung right through then repeated with the second voice, then with the third as well.
16 From *Apollonian Harmony* (c. 1790) – William Shenstone's poems were chosen as texts by several glee composers.
17 From *A Collection of Catches* (c. 1740).
18 From an C18th score in the editor's possession – ideally ttb but could also be sung ssb. If sung unaccompanied by male voices, the bass should take the optional lower octaves; if performed with continuo and/or two sopranos, then the upper octaves.
19 From *A 3rd Book of Catches, Canons and Glees* (1775) – gained a prize medal in 1772. Originally in F minor for tttb; for this satb version the soprano and tenor lines in the last two bars have been exchanged.
20 From *A Collection of Glees and Catches* (c. 1775) – for male or mixed voices.
21 From *The Musical Times*, Vo. 11, No. 260 (1864) – originally for attb in E major, in this version the alto and tenor parts have been exchanged from the second crotchet (quarter-note) of bar 17 to end of bar 20, and from the third minim (half-note) of bar 43 to the end.
22 From *A 5th Book of Canzonets, Catches, Canons & Glees* (1799) – this is an early version of the song that enjoys a modest currency as 'The stars and

stripes'. In verse 1 – ·'When this answer arriv'd, this answer arriv'd – the word 'when' has been omitted as the phrase is repeated; the same principle may usefully be applied in some subsequent verses, eg. v.IV, line 4. Ideally ttb, but could be sung ssa or stb.

23 From *Twelve Original English Glees* (c. 1810) – originally for attb in Eb major, an satb version in G major was published in 1885 with some alterations. Apart from the transposition, the version here printed follows the earlier edition.

24 From a C19th score in the editor's possession – the composer provided the alternatives given and the following explanatory note: 'In order to render this publication of general facility in performance for different gradations of voice the singers will please to observe that the three Principal Staves in the Key of "C" present the original arrangement for Two Tenors and a Bass. If a Contralto voice sings the first part, the Glee had better be sung a note higher (in D major). The Small Stave above the first line is intended for the accommodation of Soprano Voices not extending above "F". The second line may then be sung either by a Soprano or a Tenor, and by observing these directions the Glee is equally suitable to Ladies or Gentlemen'.

25 From the *Novello Part-Song Book* (1869 etc) – originally published in Germany with Mathison's German text: 'Purpur malt die Tannenhügel'.

26 Originally published by Addison & Hollier (1853) in this version; also published in C major for attb. The composer provided the following note: 'The words of this song are written in allusion to an event supposed to have taken place in the neighbourhood of Winterborne in Gloucestershire. One Hickenstirn (or Hickery Stirn, as he is called by the common people) who lies buried in the church there, is said to have been a knight who lived by pillage. He fell in love with a neighbour's daughter – won her affections – was refused by her parents – but with the assistance of his friends, carried her off from her father's house. Such events were not uncommon in the middle ages.'

27 From the *Novello Part-Song Book* (1869 etc) – this arrangement for mixed voices was made by the composer, the original for male voices was in Db major.

28 Published in *The Musical Times*, No. 272 (1844), but subsequently in various keys including an satb version (Gould & Co. 1905) in C major. Bb major is chosen as a compromise, requiring little downward transposition for male voices (Ab major is perhaps the best key).

29 From *The Novello Orpheus Series* (1900) – originally for attb in C major.

30 From *Novello Choral Songs* (1869) – was published, like No. 28, in various keys.